A Gift For:

_____

From:

_____

Copyright © Peanuts Worldwide LLC.

Published in 2019 by Hallmark Gift Books,
a division of Hallmark Cards, Inc.,
Kansas City, MO 64141
Visit us on the Web at Hallmark.com.

Editorial Director: Delia Berrigan
Art Director: Chris Opheim
Designer: Scott Swanson
Production Designer: Dan Horton
Contributing Writers: Andrew Blackburn
and Lisa Riggin

ISBN: 978-1-63059-651-4
1BOK1431

Made in China
1220

Family Is . . .

always being together.

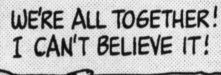

. . . reason enough to celebrate.

THIS CALLS FOR A CELEBRATION...

5-9

ROOT BEER ALL AROUND!

. . . going to always mean well.

. . . being proud of your good name.

... willing to overlook your faults.

. . . liking you just the way you are.

. **keeping in touch.**

... making room for everyone.

. . . there for you to go home to.

IT'S HARD TO TELL EVERYBODY TO GO HOME WHEN NO ONE SHOWED UP!

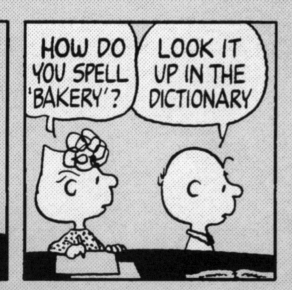

. . . a good source of advice.

. . passing
on your
best
qualities.

. . . open and honest communication.

DON'T KNOW ABOUT
OSE DISCUSSION GROUPS

I LIKE TALKING, BUT
I HATE LISTENING!

. . . always going to choose you.

BUT I'VE NEVER ASKED YOU TO CHOOSE, HAVE I?

NO, I GUESS YOU HAVEN'T

WHEW!!

7-15

. . . always staying close.

. . . a source of solid support.

'M GLAD YOU SAID
HAT... I FEEL THE SAME
AY... WHY SHOULD I
ET THEM DISCOURAGE ME?

I THINK I'LL QUIT SCHOOL!

9-16.

... where they know the real you.

...always
ready
to listen.

. . . having someone to share a meal with.

. . . the people who know your strengths.

...not the same without YOU.

I FEEL SORRY FOR THEM

7-17

WHAT FUN WAS IT WITHOUT HAVING ME AROUND?

. . . a **never-ending source of laughter.**

remembering the good old days.

SCHULZ
MAJOR FUNDING FOR THIS MEAL WAS PROVIDED BY A GRANT FROM OUR FAMILY

... always taking care of each other.

. . . loving the ones who drive you crazy.

. . not needing anyone else to laugh at your jokes.

. . . helping everyone reach his or her potential.

I REFUSE TO BELIEVE THAT MY MOTHER RAISED ME TO BE A POP-UP UMBRELLA!

8-21

. . . not always going to understand you.

. . . always being in it together.

THIS IS OUR CLASS PICTURE... THERE'S PHIL, THE BOY I TOLD YOU ABOUT WHO LOVES ME

5-9

AND THAT'S SAMMY, WHO LOVES ME, AND FRED, WHO LOVES ME, AND WILLIAM WHO LOVES ME, AND...

. . . knowing someone will always love you.

ALL THOSE BOYS LOVE YOU?

WHEN NO ONE LOVES YOU, YOU HAVE TO PRETEND THAT EVERYONE LOVES YOU!

" YOU NEVER MISS THE WATER TILL THE WELL RUNS DRY.."

THAT'S WHAT MY GRANDFATHER ALWAYS USED TO SAY

6-

. . . words of wisdom when you need them.

. . . a constant
source
of support.

. . . giving everyone a chance.

. . . having people who are the same kind of weird as you.

"YOU DON'T HAVE TO
AKE THIS TRIP," SHE
AID.."YOU CAN GO HOME!"
O HE WENT HOME!

10-30

YOUR WHOLE FAMILY'S
WEIRD, MARCIE..

HERE, SIGN THIS!

WHAT IS IT?

8-22

OUR FAMILY SHOULD HAVE HAD AN AGREEMENT LIKE THI A LONG TIME AGO...

...learning to work together.

. sharing
the
same old
sayings.

... having people who always know just what you need.

... small acts of everyday kindness.

never-ending loyalty.

. . . built-in stress relief.

. . . willing to call your bluff.

O ONE NEED EVER
E ASHAMED OF
GERNAILS MADE DIRTY
A HARD DAY'S WORK

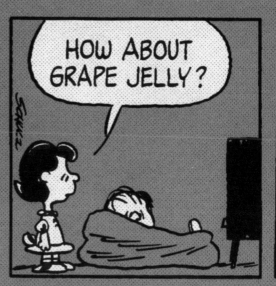

HOW ABOUT GRAPE JELLY?

... knowing where your talents come from.

. . . a balancing act.

1-31

...supportive.

HEY, BIG BROTHER, I'M MAKING OUR LUNCHES... WHAT KIND OF SANDWICH WOULD YOU LIKE?

PEANUT BUTTER WILL OKAY, I GUESS..THANK YO

. . . having your own opinions.

. . **always
there
when
you
need
them.**

OKAY, BIG BROTHER, YOUR SANDWICH IS READY... BUT I DON'T KNOW HOW YOU'RE GOING TO CARRY IT...

YOUR LUNCH BOX IS BROKEN AND WE'RE ALL OUT OF PAPER BAGS...

. resourceful.

3-23

...empathy.

NO, WE'RE TRYING TO RAISE A LITTLE MONEY, AND WE NEED SOMEONE TO SELL POPCORN...

THAT WAS WEIRD, BIG BROTHER...I COULD HEAR YOUR FACE FALL CLEAR OUT IN THE OTHER ROOM!

. . . working together.

Merry Christmas from the two of us... Charles Brown
and Sally
SCHULZ

. . . the people
who know
you best.

4-23

... worth standing up for.

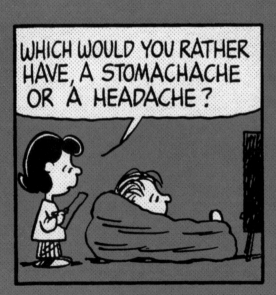
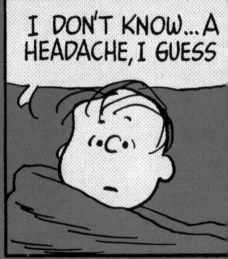

... where leaders are born.

OOD! I'LL PUT YOU
OWN FOR A HEADACHE

10-3

IT'S NICE HAVING
SOMEONE IN CHARGE
WHO'S SO CONSIDERATE

.. by your side, no matter where life takes you.

. . encour-
agement
to be the
best you
can be.

. . . where our stories begin.

And that's the story of how two soldiers and their sister met in France during World War I.

5-11

And I don't care if anyone believes me or not.

If you enjoyed this book
or it has touched your life in some way,
we'd love to hear from you.

Please write a review at Hallmark.com,
e-mail us at booknotes@hallmark.com,
or send your comments to:

Hallmark Book Feedback
P.O. Box 419034
Mail Drop 100
Kansas City, MO 64141